2
W0007441
This book belongs to
1
3

First American edition.

Published simultaneously in Canada.
A Ventura book, planned and produced by Ventura Publishing Ltd.,
27 Wrights Lane, London W8 5TZ, England.
Printed and bound in Singapore.
L.C. number: 93-77785. ISBN 0-399-22601-X.
G. P. Putnam's Sons, 200 Madison Avenue, NYC 10016.
1 3 5 7 9 10 8 6 4 2

G. P. Putnam's Sons • New York

my very own Spot Book

Hello!
This is *your* book.
Write about yourself, do
some drawings, and stick
in things you want
to keep!

Eric Hill

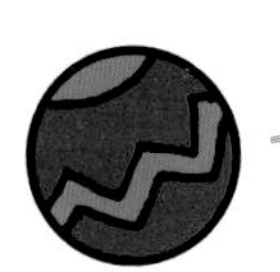

All about me

My name is

....

I was born on ....

at ....

This is where I live:

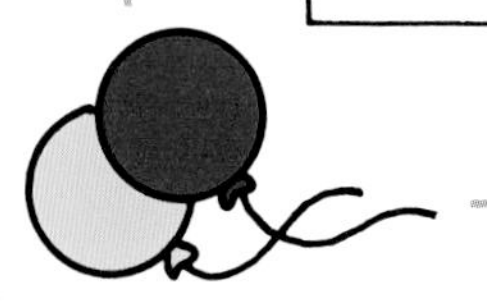

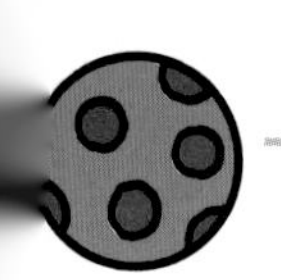

All about me

I am .... years old

My eyes are ....

My hair is ....

I am .... tall

I weigh ....

My shoe size is ....

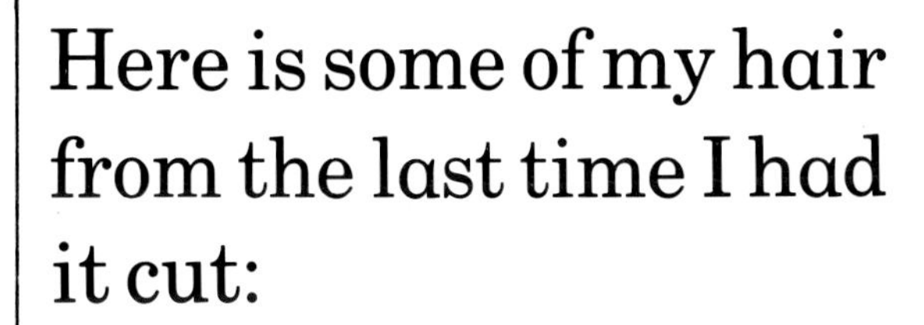

Here is some of my hair from the last time I had it cut:

All about me

This is Spot's pawprint.

Here is my handprint:

Photographs of me

My family

Spot has a mom called Sally, a dad called Sam, and a baby sister called Susie.

My family's names:

....

....

....

....

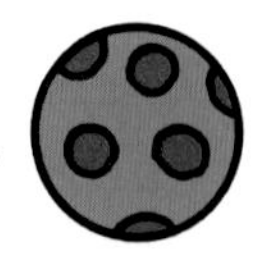

Pictures of my family

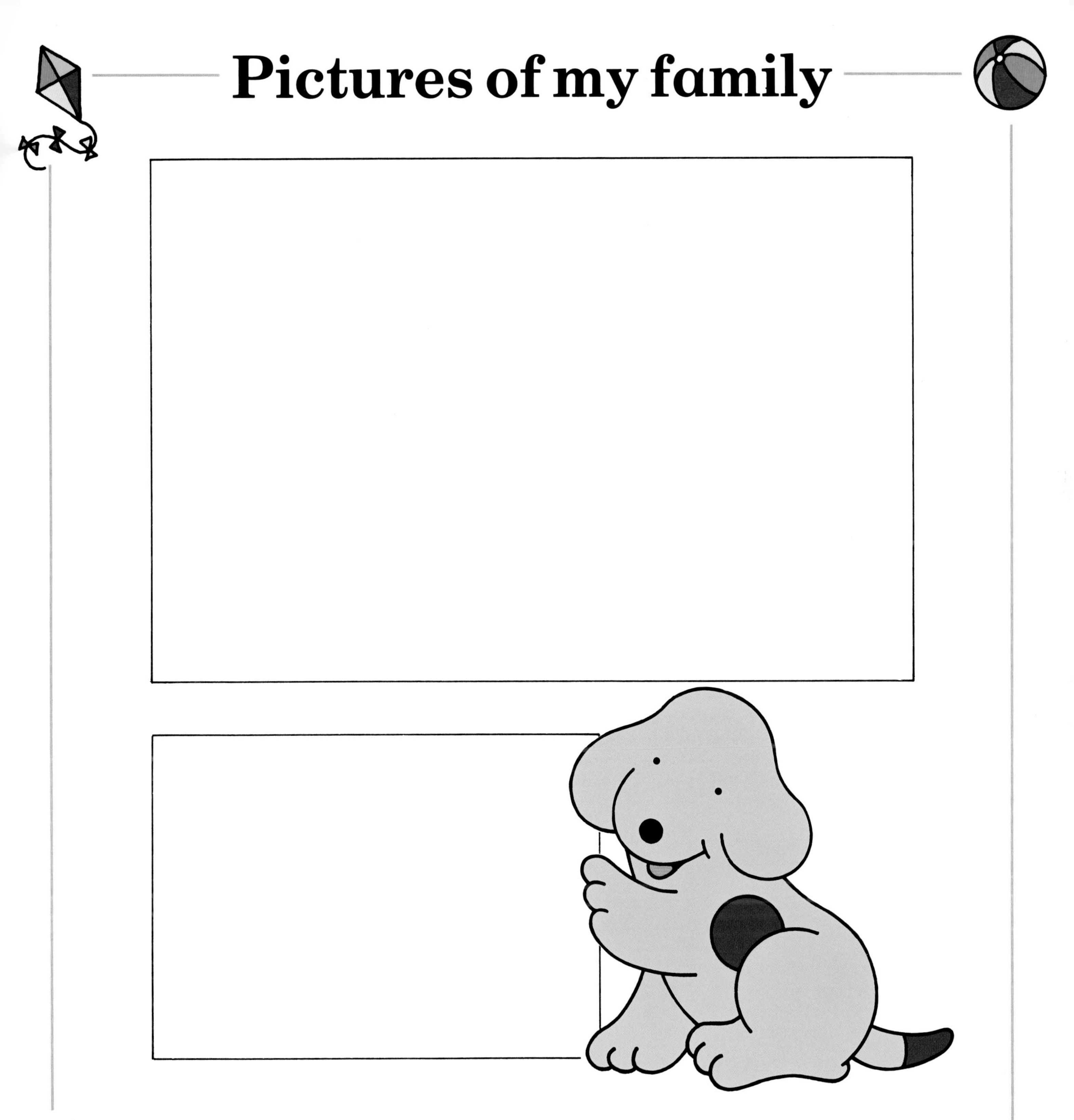

My friends

Spot's best friends are Steve, Helen and Tom.

My best friends:

....

....

....

Pictures of my friends
2

My favorites

Spot's favorite toy is his teddy.

My favorite toy is:

....

My favorite toy looks like this: